PEOPLE WHO KNEW GOD

GERTRUDE PRIESTER
Illustrated by
ERIC VON SCHMIDT

United Church Press
Boston · Philadelphia

CONTENTS

Dear Boys and Girls:

Have you ever gone outside on a dark night to look at the stars, or to watch a satellite move across the sky? Have you wondered if you will ever see for yourself what is out beyond the stars?

Standing there, looking at the sky and the stars, have you wondered about God? If you have, you are like thousands of other people. People have always wondered about God, and people are still trying to find out more about him and his purpose for his world.

The stories in this book have something to tell you about God. Some of them are about Bible people who lived long, long ago. Some are about the men and women who worked hard to help people believe in Jesus when the Christian church was still very young. And others tell about people who may be like some of your neighbors.

These people have known God and believed in him. Because of this, they have done some amazing things.

As you read about these men and women, these boys and girls, ask yourself, "What are they telling me about God? What is God like if he caused them to act as they did?"

When you have finished the book, ask yourself, "Do my friends and my family ever learn anything about God from me?" You may be surprised at your answer.

Gertrude Priester

ABRAHAM

Three thousand years ago, Abraham, the chief of a tribe of shepherds, led his people a great distance across desert lands to find pasture for their animals and a home for their families.

But this was not the only reason they made such a long journey. The main reason was that God had promised to make Abraham's people a great nation if they would do as he commanded. And God had commanded them to travel to a new land that would be their home.

————

ONE DAY as Abraham stood in the doorway of his tent, he saw three shepherds hurrying towards him. "There's trouble somewhere," said Abraham to himself. "Nothing but trouble

2

would make those men walk so fast in the heat of the day."

As soon as the greetings were over, the first man spoke. "One of our wells has gone dry," he said. "We'll have to find others or our flocks will die of thirst."

"Last night a wolf killed one of our sheep," the second reported.

"Lot's men are giving us trouble again," said the third. "When we take our sheep and goats for water, his men push in ahead of us. And when we are ready to move our herds to a new grazing spot, they always get there first."

"Go in peace," said Abraham. "I will see what I can do."

After the shepherds had gone, he sat down in the doorway to think. "It is a hard job to be the leader of such a big tribe," he said

to himself. "Perhaps my work will be easier if I remind my people why we are in this place."

He clapped his hands together. At the signal a boy appeared.

"Tonight at the campfire I must talk to all our people," he said to the boy. "Go quickly from tent to tent and tell everyone. Let the other boys help you so that no one is missed. Go yourself to my nephew Lot. Tell him to come with all his people. Everyone must be there except those who watch over the herds," he commanded.

The boys ran from tent to tent. To every family they gave the message, "Abraham wants to talk to the whole tribe. Tonight you must gather around the campfire to hear what he will say."

As the sun went down, the tribesmen gathered. In the circle nearest the fire were the men, the fathers of families. Close behind them were the young men and the boys. The girls and the women, many carrying their babies in their arms, sat on the outside of the circle. Abraham asked Lot to sit beside him.

Abraham looked around the circle at the whole tribe sitting together in the firelight. "My children," he began, "you all know we have had some trouble over the wells and the grazing land. Lot and I will look for a way to put an end to this in the morning. We will ask God to help us do this."

There was a sigh of relief among the people, for the fights among the shepherds had frightened them. They trusted Abraham; they knew that he would do what he promised. Now they waited to hear what he would say next.

"You remember that we have not always lived in this good land," said Abraham. "Many years ago we lived in the great city of Haran. Tonight I want to tell you once again how God spoke to me, saying, 'Go from your country and your people and your father's house to the land that I will show you.'" Abraham paused, almost as if he were hearing God's words again.

"I started out with my flocks and my family, not knowing where I was going. But I trusted God and through all the years he has kept his promise. Here our families have grown bigger, and our flocks have increased until now the land can no longer provide all of us with enough to eat.

"There was another part of God's message on that day so long ago in Haran. I heard him say, 'I will make of you a great nation, and through you all the nations of the world shall be blessed.' This part of his promise has not yet come true."

Abraham straightened up. "But God is good, and I trust his word," he said. "God has led us through the years past. He has kept his promise to bring us to a good land and he will continue to lead us. Remember this as you go back to your tents."

The next morning Abraham and Lot met on a hillside. Together they looked off across the countryside. Lot was ready to fight for his fair share of the best pasture and the deepest wells.

7

Abraham said, "There is plenty of pasture for both of us. We must divide it so that your men know which is your part and my men know which is ours. This will end the fighting among them."

The two men climbed higher to get a better view. Lot was surprised when Abraham said, "You choose the part you want, and I will take what is left." Abraham was the chief of the tribe! By rights he should have the first choice.

"If he wants to do it this way, that's his business," muttered Lot as he looked around to see which part of the land was best. Off to the east he saw the grass was greenest. That meant there were good wells there too. He chose that part.

8

Abraham agreed, and Lot began to move his tents and his herds to the land he had chosen. Abraham called his men together and pointed off to the west to the hilly country. "There is our pasture, and there are the wells that we shall use. Do not go beyond these rocks to the east, for all that section belongs to Lot."

The men did as Abraham asked. The trouble was ended, and life was peaceful once more.

After Lot and all his people and their flocks had gone to the green valley, Abraham again heard God speaking to him. This time the message was a little different. "Look all around you, to the north and to the south, to the east and to the west. All the land you see I will give to you and to your children's children forever. Your descendants shall be as many as the dust of the earth."

Abraham thanked God for his promise, although he did not yet see how he could have descendants as he did not have even one son. Abraham and his wife Sarah had hoped for many years to have a child to lead the tribe after they were gone, but their greatest wish had not been granted. Nevertheless, Abraham trusted God. The promise would surely come true. Someday he would have a son.

FOR YOU TO READ IN YOUR BIBLE

There is more to the story of Abraham. Maybe you know what happened, and whether or not God kept his promise. If you would like to read about it in your Bible, look at verses 2, 3, and 8 in Genesis 21.

A
PRAYER
FOR YOU TO USE
AT MEALTIME

THANK YOU, God,
for all your care.

THANK YOU for food,
and for our home,
and for mother
and father
who love us.

THANK YOU, God,
for your great love.
Amen.

*(Written by a junior vacation
church school class)*

RANDY MAKES A DISCOVERY

The door to Miss Carey's fourth-grade classroom stood wide open as Randy walked slowly down the big, empty hall. Randy kicked his shoe against the wall. He banged on every door along the way. And as he walked through the door into Miss Carey's room, he pulled so hard at his coat buttons that the top one popped off and disappeared under his teacher's desk. Randy made a dive for it and was lucky enough to find it.

Just as Randy got up from the floor, he saw Mike's four-color pencil lying right beside his foot. Randy picked up the pencil and pushed down on the button with the little red dot. Out popped the point that wrote in red. He found a piece of paper and on it wrote R-A-N-D-Y. Then he pushed out the point that wrote in green. R-A-N-D-Y in green looked even better! Next he tried the blue, and then the black points.

12

"I sure wish I had one of these," thought Randy, turning the pencil round and round to look at all the colored dots. "It's the best kind there is." He started to lay the pencil down on Mike's desk but just then he heard a shout from the playground. He frowned, remembering how Miss Carey had asked him to leave the game and come back to the room alone.

"OK. So they don't want me in their old ball game, just because I won't wait all day for my turn to pitch. Those other guys can't pitch anyway. It's a waste of time to even give them a turn. I'll get even with them. That old Mike thinks he's so good just because . . ." Randy looked again at the pencil that he still held in his hand. He looked at Mike's desk, then at the floor, and then back at the desk.

"Say," said Randy right out loud, "I think maybe I've just found me a pencil. Nobody would leave his pencil on the floor if he still wanted it. Anyway, finders keepers. Go ahead, you guys. Stay out there and play ball. Who cares? Not me! I'll be sort of busy anyway, using my new pencil." And off he went to hang up his coat.

Soon the rest of the fourth grade came back to their room. It was time for another of the stories about great men that Miss Carey read aloud to the class.

14

Everyone gathered in the reading corner except Mike. "Come along, Mike," said the teacher, "we're waiting."

"I can't find my pencil," mumbled Mike, his head halfway under his chair. "It was right here when we went outside. You told me not to take it out in case it might drop out of my pocket and get lost. It was right here. I know it was."

"We'll all help you look for it after our story," promised Miss Carey.

15

Later, when a thorough search of the room failed to turn up the missing pencil, Miss Carey asked the class to return to their desks. After everyone was seated, she looked all around without saying a single word. Randy was sure that she looked more at him than at the others. "Anyway it's mine," he said to himself. "Finders keepers. It's OK."

At last Miss Carey spoke. "You know, boys and girls, we are a little like a family in this room. We know each other very well and we spend many hours together each day. Some of you have special friends here whom you like better than anyone else. But there never was a group of people anywhere who didn't have to work at the business of getting along together. What do you think is causing our trouble in getting along in this class?"

For a minute no one said anything. Then Sally spoke up. "Well, we get tired of some people always wanting to be first, and pushing in ahead of everybody else all the time." She looked right at Randy, who pretended not to be listening.

John said, "I guess that sometimes we gang up on the fellows who make us mad."

"But it's their own fault," said Ricky. "If they would only wait and play fair like everyone else, we wouldn't have to treat them like that."

"Somebody in this room *stole* my pencil," exploded Mike, "and I think I know who did it. Just you wait. I'll get him. You wait and see."

Miss Carey held up her hand. "Sometimes we get angrier and angrier until we feel as if we could blow up. I know how you feel, Mike. But we have a rule in this room about saying that someone stole something."

"You have to be able to prove it before you say it," said Ricky. "But Mike's pencil *was* here when we went out for recess. I saw it when I went to give him back the crayons I had borrowed."

"All that is true, I'm sure," said Miss Carey. "But if anyone in this room *did* take your pencil, Mike, that person must have had some very mixed-up feelings, and maybe those feelings made

the person decide to take something that did not belong to him."

"You mean somebody had a reason for taking my pencil?" said Mike.

"He couldn't have had a *right* reason," said Sally. "Stealing's never right."

"Maybe somebody doesn't like you, Mike," said Randy. "Sometimes you're sort of bossy."

"Or maybe somebody didn't have enough money to buy a pencil," said Betsy.

"Once I threw my sister's best doll down the stairs because my brother had stepped on the ladder from my fire truck and broken it," said Mike. "I just wanted to do something to some-one else, I felt so mad."

"You all know what I mean by mixed-up feelings, I can see that," said Miss Carey, "so you probably all can remember how hard it is to get going in the right direction after those mixed-up feelings have made you do something wrong. But if we really want to learn to get along together in this class, I can think of one way we can help each other when we get into these mix-ups. Can you guess what I am thinking about?"

Betsy raised her hand. "Maybe you're thinking that we shouldn't have mixed-up feelings in the first place," she said.

Miss Carey shook her head. "No, that's just not the way people are. We all do have them, and there's no use pretending that we can say some magic word and then never have unhappy or mean feelings again. But I'll give you a clue. Suppose I did something unkind to you, Betsy, and then I decided to admit I had done wrong and I was sorry. Is that all there is to it?"

"Oh, no," said Ricky. "The other person has to say that it's OK again or the trouble's still there."

"That's just what I'm thinking," said Miss Carey. "It is hard enough to admit you're wrong and say you are sorry. But if you can't count on people being willing to forgive you, then it is a lot harder."

"If anyone tells me he took my pencil, I'll punch him in the nose," said Mike.

"I would never tell you then," said Ricky laughing. "You must not want that pencil back."

"I do too want it back," said Mike. "But, well—maybe I'd think about it first. *Maybe* I wouldn't punch him very hard."

"Thinking about it is a good idea," said Miss Carey. "Here comes the bus, so I guess I'll have to read our new story some other day. But I want to ask each of you to do one thing for your homework tonight. Go off by yourself where no one will bother

21

you, and just *think* about what we have been saying. And tomorrow we will see if we have any ideas about how to straighten out
our mix-up. Good-by, now. Be careful crossing the streets."

FOR YOU TO THINK ABOUT

Some boys and girls who read this story will not like it at all.
They will want to know how it comes out in the end. But that
is too easy. Most of the time when we get into trouble, as Randy
did, no one knows just how it will turn out. It depends on what
people think and do.

Try to think of some of the ways this story might end. What
could Randy do? What could Mike do? What could the class do?
Do you think the children might act in different ways? If you
were Randy, how would you want the story to end? If you were
one of the other boys and girls, what would you want the ending
to be? Do you know why the children acted the way they did
toward Randy? Have you ever had anything like this happen to
you? Why did you do what you did?

A
PRAYER
FOR YOU
TO PRAY WHEN
THINGS ARE
GOING ALL
WRONG

DEAR GOD, help me
to remember how it feels when
someone is unfair or
gets angry with me.
If I have treated someone
this way, help me
to tell him that I am sorry.
If others are making me unhappy,
help me to think of what
I can do about it
if some of the fault is mine.
Thank you for
loving me even when I
do wrong.

Amen.

23

NEWS OF JEREMIAH

Some of the people in the Bible who came to know God best were called prophets. A prophet is a person who speaks for God. Many times these men were very unpopular because they reminded the people that they were doing wrong in the eyes of God. Often the people did not pay attention to what the prophets said, and went right on doing what they had been warned not to do.

One of these prophets, a man named Jeremiah, was hated by the people to whom he spoke. He faced angry mobs. He was thrown into prison. He became so discouraged that he told God he was sorry he had ever become a prophet. And yet Jeremiah could not stop speaking out for God!

If there had been radio and TV in those days, all the newsmen would have wanted to talk with the prophets. Let's pretend that there was TV then. Let's pretend that you are watching a program about horsemen out in the desert. Here are some news flashes that might break into your program.

NEWS BULLETIN, JERUSALEM, 604 B.C.

Crowds around the temple were startled today when they were told that our country will soon be overcome by an enemy from the north. Baruch, the prophet Jeremiah's secretary, stood at an upper window overlooking the temple gate and read these strange words, "A nation whose words you do not understand shall destroy you with the sword."

The scroll from which he was reading was seized and was rushed at once to King Jehoiakim.

News Bulletin

King Jehoiakim is furious! He has burned the scroll which Baruch read yesterday at the temple. As fast as it was read to him, the king cut off parts of it with his knife and threw it into the fire burning before him.

When it was learned that the scroll had been dictated by Jeremiah, the king ordered that both Jeremiah and his secretary Baruch be thrown into prison.

News Bulletin

The king's officers cannot find Jeremiah and Baruch. The prophet and his secretary seem to have disappeared after the burning of the scroll yesterday.

The king is still angry, and has ordered that the men be found. It is said that the princes fear Jeremiah's dreadful words may be true.

——————————————

These princes, who half believed what Jeremiah said, warned him to stay in hiding. His life was not safe as long as Jehoiakim was king. But while in hiding Jeremiah did not waste his time. He dictated again to Baruch all that had been written on the scroll that the king had burned.

Let's turn on our TV of long ago once more. Now there is a new king, Zedekiah. Perhaps there will be more news of Jeremiah.

——————————————

NEWS BULLETIN, JERUSALEM, 589 B.C.

Jeremiah says the nation faces defeat! The prophet warns that our city will fall to the enemy. "Do not put your faith in the soldiers," he says. "You must put your trust in God."

NEWS BULLETIN

Unrest in the king's army is reported. Jeremiah's words about the defeat of the city have upset the soldiers. "Why risk our lives if everyone is going to be captured anyway?" they ask.

The princes are insisting that Jeremiah be put to death for betraying his country.

NEWS COMMENTATOR'S SPECIAL STORY

This morning the princes and the king met to decide what to do with Jeremiah. Some of the princes wanted to kill him right then and there. But it was decided that he should have a worse punishment, to show all the people that it did not pay to be a traitor.

At noon today Jeremiah was taken from the prison and put down into a slimy, dirty well. There he is to remain until he starves to death.

NEWS BULLETIN: SPECIAL REPORT ON JEREMIAH

Word has been received that the prophet Jeremiah has been rescued from the well where he was placed earlier today. Reports have come in that he was seen being lifted out by a stranger. Some say that the king gave his permission for this man to take Jeremiah away and keep him out of danger. A crowd is gathering around the well and soldiers are on duty to keep order.

Stay tuned to this station for on-the-scene reports which will be broadcast as soon as the soldiers allow our cameramen through to get some pictures. Our regular programs will be interrupted whenever we have further news as to the whereabouts of Jeremiah. He cannot have been taken far because he and his rescuer were on foot.

LATE NEWS FLASH

We now know that the king himself sent three of his own servants to help the stranger who rescued Jeremiah earlier today. People are asking what made the king change his mind about the prophet.

It is reported that when Jeremiah was raised from the well he was still talking about God. "Obey the word of the Lord, and your life will be spared. If you do not listen to the word of the Lord, Jerusalem will be destroyed!"

Every day the enemy grows stronger. Could Jeremiah be right?

A PRAYER

DEAR GOD,
we thank you
for all the people
who have been
brave enough
to do what they felt
you wanted them to do,
even though
this was difficult.

HELP US
to know that
you will give us
courage to do our best
even when
it is not easy.
Amen.

PAUL RETURNS TO JERUSALEM

One of the greatest heroes of the Christian church is a man named Paul.

If you will turn to the book of Acts in your Bible, in the last three verses in chapter 7 you can read what is first told about this man Paul. He is called Saul in these verses. Only later, after he became a Christian, did he come to be known as Paul.

The rest of his story is found in the chapters that follow. They tell how Saul at first hated the Christians so much that he hunted them out of their homes, broke up their worship services, and put them in prison when they refused to give up their belief in Jesus. Even the sound of Saul's name was enough to frighten the early Christians, for it always meant trouble. Saul honestly thought he was doing God's will in trying to get rid of these followers of Jesus.

One day all this was suddenly changed. On his way to Damascus to hunt out some more Christians, something happened to Saul that made him understand about Jesus. Then he knew he had been wrong and the Christians were right. This story you will hear in your church school class.

From then on, Paul got into a great deal of trouble just because he felt he *must* speak out for Jesus no matter how dangerous it was to do so. He made a great many enemies. The Jews hated him. People who believed in many gods hated him. And people who believed in no god hated him. Even some of the Christians hated him because he did not always agree with them. But nothing stopped Paul. He knew God's love and had to speak for him.

Here is a true story about one of Paul's dangerous adventures. It is found in the Bible in Chapters 21, 22, and 23 of the book of Acts.

———

THE SUN beat down on the dusty road. Tired and hot, a little group of men walked slowly toward the city of Jerusalem.

"You come with me, Paul," said one of the men. "We can stay with one of my friends. You will be safe there. He has heard all about you and wants to be your friend."

36

Paul smiled. "There are not many like him in this city, are there? I hope he can arrange a meeting for me with the leaders of the church right away. I want to tell them how many people are becoming Christians. And I must deliver this gift of money the new churches have collected to help their Christian friends here in Jerusalem."

As the men came near the gate of the city, Paul looked around him. Suddenly he shivered. He stopped right in the middle of the street. He closed his eyes. He was remembering the day when he had come outside this very gate to watch a Christian die. Even now the memory was almost too much for Paul. He could still see Stephen lying on the ground, bleeding and hurt, with the stones flying around him.

It was Stephen's bravery that had made him first wonder if the Christians were right about Jesus. As Paul opened his eyes and walked on, he thought of all the times he had been in danger since the day when he, too, became a follower of Jesus.

"I wonder if there will be another stoning here," he said to himself. "There are still many Jews who are angry at the Christians as I used to be. Besides that, there are Christians who do not like what I have done. Will I be the next to be stoned because I must tell people about Jesus Christ?"

He did not have long to wonder. He made his reports to the church leaders and delivered the gifts of money. Then instead of staying out of sight, he went to the temple where his enemies caught him preaching in the courtyard. Their shouts and angry words drew more and more people. Before long Paul was in the middle of a howling, screaming mob.

"Kill him! Get rid of the dog!" they shouted.

"We'll kill him if we can get to him," others screamed as they hunted for stones.

Caught in the mob, beaten and kicked, Paul fell to the ground. As he was being dragged out of the courtyard, a Roman soldier came running to see what was happening. When he saw the crowd, he knew he must have help.

"No one knows when these crazy Jews will get excited," he muttered. "Come help me!" he called to some soldiers who came around the corner of the temple just then. "We must stop this fight right away or it will get out of hand."

As the soldiers began to beat back the mob with their swords, they saw Paul lying on the ground. "There he is! Get that man! He's the cause of it all. He must be a dangerous fellow."

"Bind him with two chains," ordered the commander. "Take him to the barracks. We'll find out soon enough who he is and what he's done."

As the soldiers started off with Paul, the mob crowded forward, trying to get their hands on him again. Only the soldiers' sharp swords kept Paul from being dragged back into the angry mob.

Just as he was about to be taken into the barracks, Paul spoke to the commander. "May I have a word with you?" he asked.

"Yes, if you are quick about it," replied the officer. "Who are you anyway?"

"I am a Jew," answered Paul, "and I beg you to let me speak to these people."

The commander agreed, hoping to learn something more about the cause of all the fighting. Paul tried to explain to the crowd

what he believed, but they would not listen. In the middle of his speech their shouts and screams became so loud that the commander ordered his men to take Paul into the barracks.

There the soldiers were just about to beat him to make him

confess his crime, when Paul spoke again. "Are you allowed to beat a Roman citizen before he has had a chance to speak?"

"Stop!" commanded the officer when he heard what Paul had said. "Let me talk to that man." He went over to Paul. "Are you really a Roman citizen?" he asked.

"Yes," answered Paul firmly.

The soldiers stood back and looked at Paul. A Roman citizen must be given a chance to tell his side of the story. This was the law of the land.

The next day the commander summoned the chief priests and the council to hear Paul's story. As Paul began to speak, the Jews started again to argue and shout at one another. Some said Paul had done nothing wrong while others tried to seize him and drag him away. The fight became so violent that the soldiers were afraid Paul would be torn to pieces. They surrounded him and took him back to the prison to keep him safe.

Paul's nephew, who lived in Jerusalem, found out that there was a plot to capture Paul when he was again brought out to be questioned. Forty men had agreed neither to eat nor drink until they had killed him. When this was reported to the commander, he knew that Paul was too dangerous a prisoner to be kept in Jerusalem.

He called two of his men. "Get ready two hundred soldiers with seventy horsemen and two hundred men armed with spears. Tonight when it is dark and the city is quiet, you are to take the prisoner Paul away. See that he gets safely to the Roman governor. I will give you a letter to take to him, explaining what has happened. The governor will see that Paul has a fair chance to tell his story."

As he rode off in the middle of the night, protected by the Roman soldiers, Paul was thinking, "Perhaps I shall never be free again. But no matter what they do to me, I know God will give me strength to bear it. I know that neither life nor death can separate me from the love of God in Christ Jesus. I will talk about his love whenever I get the chance. There is nothing more important to me in the whole world, not even my own life!"

A
PRAYER FOR
YOU TO PRAY WHEN
YOU MUST MAKE
A HARD
DECISION

DEAR GOD, help me
to take time to think
about the choices I can make.
Help me to think
not only of myself,
but of other people too.
Help me to think
about what may happen to them
and to myself when I make
my choice. Help me to
make a good choice, O God,
and to be strong enough to
stand by it.
Thank you for your love and
help that are always with me.
Amen.

45

THE STORY OF TELEMACHUS

Have you ever seen a movie or heard a story about how brave the first Christians were? Did you ever stop to wonder about them or to imagine what they were like? It is hard for us to remember that they were men and women, boys and girls, just like us. They lived in homes where their children played together and where their friends came to visit. They did not want to get into trouble with the leaders of their country or of their church. And they did not want to suffer for their faith. But they were sure of one thing—they must worship God in the way they believed to be right.

Believing in God's way of love often got the early Christians into trouble, because they could not just *believe* with their heads —they had to *do* something about it. There is a story about a man with a long name—Te-lem'-a-chus—who also thought that every Christian should show his beliefs by his actions. As you read about him, you can decide whether you think his own life proved this to be true.

———————

ONCE LONG AGO, when the Christian church was still very new, an old, old man named Telemachus started out on a long trip. All his life he had dreamed about visiting the city of Rome. Now, at last, he was on his way.

He walked for many days along the dusty roads in the burning sun. Often he had to stop to rest, but each day he came closer to the greatest city in all the world.

One morning, he saw far ahead of him the outlines of many buildings. "It must be Rome," he cried out loud. "I am almost there." He began to walk a little faster.

As he came closer to the great city, he found that the road was becoming crowded with people. But strangely enough they were all coming *out* of the city!

Old Telemachus made his way through the crowds, bumped and shoved about until he was almost too tired to go on. Finally he stopped to rest a moment, and to look about him. Then he called to one of the men passing by, "Where are you going? And why are all these people leaving the city?"

"We're going to see the fight," shouted the man. "You don't want to miss this. It's great fun. Come along with us."

Telemachus looked toward Rome. Then he looked at the excited crowd. "I've waited many years to see the city," he thought. "I guess a few more hours won't make any difference." So he turned back along the road and pushed with the crowd toward a place that looked like a huge playing field. There he found a place high up among the many rows of seats that circled the big field below.

Before long, two big, strong men came out onto the field. Each one carried a large shield and a long spear. The crowd shouted as the two men faced each other, getting ready to fight.

At first Telemachus did not quite understand what the two men were going to do. But suddenly, as he listened to the shouts of the crowd, he knew that right before his eyes those two men on the field were going to fight each other until one of them was killed!

48

"So this is what the crowd calls fun!" thought Telemachus.
"Making men fight to the death just to amuse these people is a
terrible thing." Without stopping to think, the old man stood
up. He waved his arms and called out in a loud voice, "Stop!
Stop! In the name of Christ, stop!"

"Hush, old man," said the people around him as they tried to push him back into his seat. "You're bothering the fighters. Sit down and be quiet."

The fighters looked up when they heard the noise, but they only laughed when they saw an old man waving his arms.

Then Telemachus pushed the people away and started down the steps toward the fighters. "Stop! Stop! In the name of Christ, stop!" he kept shouting. "You must stop this killing."

As he tried to force his way between the two fighters, one of them pushed him aside and said, "Go away, old man. I'll have to run my spear through you if you don't stop bothering us."

Telemachus refused to move. The crowd began to laugh. They shouted names at him, but still he stood his ground.

Then one of the fighters took a step forward and ran his spear through Telemachus. Suddenly there was silence. Not a sound was heard from the great crowd as they watched the old man's body fall slowly to the ground. He didn't move. Telemachus was dead.

Then someone high up in the rows of seats stood up and slowly walked out, his head bowed in shame. Another person followed, then another and another. Very quietly more and more people left, until the whole place was empty.

That was the last fight in which one man had to kill another, while a crowd looked on and enjoyed the sight. Men gave up practicing to be killers of other men merely to amuse people. Leaders no longer were able to arrange fights between two human beings according to the old rule that one man must die before the fight would be declared ended. And all of this happened because one old man risked his life to do what he believed was right.

For You to Think About

Do you think that Telemachus had any idea that his act would make him a hero? Do you think he would have done what he did if there had been no crowd around to see him? Is it easier to do something brave when you know that people are watching you?

54

A PRAYER FOR YOU TO PRAY

DEAR GOD, help me to be strong enough to help other people when they are in trouble. Help me to remember some of the brave people who risked their lives because they believed in your great love. Help me to try to show that I believe in your love too.

Amen.

CARLO'S FIRST THANKSGIVING

A cold wind was blowing down the narrow street. A few flakes of wet snow stuck on the tip of Carlo's nose as he crouched in the little doorway. He shivered and tried to pull his coat up higher around his neck.

"Why did our family have to move to this big city?" he thought. "Why couldn't we have stayed in our own country where it is sunny and warm most of the time?"

As Carlo thought about the sunny streets where he used to run and play, he remembered the fruit stands where a friendly peddler would always have a banana for a hungry boy. He rubbed his stomach and wished that he could think of some way to get something to eat right now. There was nothing at home—he had already asked his mother about that.

"Nobody here would give you as much as a candy bar," he grumbled to himself as he looked longingly at the candy piled high in the window of the five-and-ten-cent store.

Carlo gave his coat another tug and started to walk slowly down the windy street. Old Jack, the newsman, was standing in his little shelter on the corner, putting bricks and stones on his piles of newspapers to keep them from blowing away.

"Hi! Carlo!" he said. "All ready for Thanksgiving at your house? Are you going to have a turkey?"

Carlo shook his head. "I don't think so," he said. "Does a turkey cost very much?"

Old Jack laughed. "For a family with six hungry kids like yours, it would take a big turkey, Carlo. And I guess that would cost more than you've got."

Carlo turned away and stood watching the traffic lights turn red, green, yellow, and back to red again. "I'll race the light," he decided, and ran across the street just as a waiting car began to move.

"Crazy kid!" shouted the driver. "Some day you'll get hurt doing that. Can't you find anything better to do?"

Carlo paid no attention. He looked down at his feet, and saw that one of his big toes had popped right out the end of his shoe as he had run across the street.

"There's no money for shoes this month," his mother had said that very morning when he had shown her how worn his

were. "We have to save enough to pay the rent or we won't even have a place to sleep. Maybe your father will find a better job soon and we'll have a little more money. But everything costs so much here in the United States, Carlo!"

The boy moved on, bending to protect his face from the wind. He watched his big toe poke out of his shoe every time he took a step.

"Ouch! Look where you're going, boy. You nearly knocked me down!" said a woman's voice. Carlo had run headlong into a lady carrying a large bag full of groceries.

He said nothing, but watched while she changed her hold on

the grocery bag and started to walk on. The loaf of fresh bread sticking up over the top of the bag had smelled so good!

As he sighed and started to walk on down the street, his foot kicked something soft. He bent over and picked up a black wallet. Quickly he looked inside, then stuck the wallet in his pocket and ducked into the nearest doorway. First, he looked all around to be sure no one was watching. Then he began to count the money. He wasn't very familiar with American money, but he could count *how many* pieces of paper money there were.

"Seven, eight, nine," counted Carlo. "Maybe there's enough to buy a turkey! What shall I do—take it home to my mother? No, she will want to keep it to pay the rent!"

Then he had an idea. "I know," he said out loud, "I'll get old Jack to help me buy a turkey. Then I'll take it home and surprise mother! What if my turkey is so big I can't carry it myself? Then I'll have to get someone to help me." Pretending that he had bought the turkey and was carrying it home, Carlo walked down the street staggering under his heavy load, with the black wallet safely pushed into his coat pocket.

Suddenly a blue police car pulled up to the curb and moved slowly along beside Carlo. At first the boy paid no attention. Police were always looking around for someone. But then he heard a woman's voice say, "There he is. That's the boy." Before he knew what was happening, Carlo was pushed into the police car and driven off to the nearest police station.

The voice he had heard belonged to the lady he had bumped into on the street, and so did the wallet. At the police station she stood nearby while the officer asked Carlo if he had the wallet. She watched while he pulled it slowly from his pocket. And she listened while Carlo tried to explain that he hadn't *stolen* the wallet, he had only picked it up off the sidewalk.

"What were you going to do with the money?" she asked.

Carlo kept his head down. He didn't want anyone to see the tears that were beginning to roll down his cheeks. He wanted his mother! But what would she say when she found out he was in trouble with the police? How did he ever get into this mix-up anyway?

"What were you going to spend the money for?" the lady asked again.

"A turkey," mumbled Carlo wiping his eyes with his dirty hand. And then the tears began to pour down his face. Nine years old or not, being all alone with a lot of strangers in a police station and not knowing what was going to happen next was no fun. "I want to go home to my mother," he wailed.

The lady made a sign to the policemen, and they left her alone with Carlo. "Come over here and sit down," she said, taking him by the hand.

They sat on a long bench and the lady asked him all kinds of questions. At first Carlo could hardly talk because he was crying

so hard. But the lady didn't seem to be in any hurry, and she listened as though she really wanted to know about him.

Finally Carlo started to tell her how his family had come to the United States only a few months before, and how the wonderful job a friend had promised his father had not been wonderful at all. He told her how his father and mother and all six children lived in two little rooms, and how there was no place to play, and no warm clothes because they had never had to wear heavy coats in their own country—and on and on until he came to the part about wanting turkey for Thanksgiving! That made Carlo remember about his mother and he started to cry all over again!

"Don't cry, Carlo," said the lady. "Wait here a minute. Then I think perhaps we can go home."

She walked over to talk to one of the policemen who had come back into the room. She was back soon, saying, "Come along, Carlo, I don't think you meant to steal my wallet. And now that I have it back, there won't be any more trouble. The police will take us to your house and I'll explain everything to your mother."

So they climbed into the police car again, and soon Carlo was leading the lady up the stairs. "Mother," he shouted as they started down the hallway toward No. 16, "Mother, here's someone to see you."

His mother opened the door, and Carlo started to tell her what had happened. But he talked so fast the words got all mixed up. Finally the lady and his mother sat down together in one corner of the room while Carlo kept the other children quiet in another corner. He tried hard to hear what they were saying, but he could catch only a few words now and then. "Our church," the lady kept saying, and "a place for the children to play." But when he heard her say "turkey dinner" he couldn't keep quiet.

He walked over and stood beside her. "How much money does it take to buy a turkey?" he asked.

The lady smiled. "It takes quite a lot of money, Carlo, and it would take a big pan and a big oven to cook it," she said, looking at the tiny gas plate standing on the table. "But I know how you can have your turkey dinner without having to buy a turkey." Then she told Carlo what she had been telling his mother. The boy could hardly believe his ears!

"Every year the people in the church where I work try to help newcomers to the United States who live here in our neighborhood. We invite them to a real Thanksgiving dinner with turkey and all the other good things that go with it. So if you will come to the church at two o'clock on Thanksgiving Day, I'll be waiting for you and we can all have dinner together.

"I'll show you the other rooms in the church, too. There is a place to play games, and a gymnasium where you can play basketball. There are rooms where your brothers and sisters can listen to stories, or learn to use tools or to sew. I am there every day to help boys and girls have a good time. We have church services on Sunday and sometimes during the week."

Carlo was too excited to hear any more. He could hardly wait to see this church where so much was going on. He could hardly wait for his first Thanksgiving in the United States!

FOR YOU TO THINK ABOUT

Do you know the story about the Pilgrim Fathers and the first Thanksgiving? Do you remember why they celebrated with a big dinner? And do you remember how they gave thanks to God for his loving care?

Sometimes we forget that each year in many cities and towns there are people who are having their very first Thanksgiving in the United States. Many of these people need help in understanding what Thanksgiving is all about. And like Carlo and his family in the true story you just read, some of these people could not have a Thanksgiving dinner if church people did not remember and care enough about them to help.

A THANKSGIVING PRAYER

DEAR GOD, thank you for our homes and
   for our mothers and fathers who love us.
THANK YOU for the days when we are happy,
AND thank you for the people who help us when we
   get into trouble or when nothing seems to go right.
THANK YOU for our school and our teachers,
AND thank you for making us so we can use our
   heads and learn to decide about right and wrong things.
THANK YOU for our friends, and for all
   the people who do things for us.
THANK YOU for our special Thanksgiving Day
   and for the good food we will eat.
HELP US to remember to share our money and
   to show that we care about other people who
   do not have as much as we do.
THANK YOU, God, for your love, and for
   our church where we learn about Jesus.
THANK YOU, God, for everything.   Amen.

THE STRANGEST CHRISTMAS

Close your eyes for a minute and ask yourself, "What do I like best about Christmas?" Then ask yourself, "Could I celebrate Christmas even though I could not have the part of it I just chose as best?"

It is hard for us to imagine Christmas without presents, a Christmas tree, carols, special church services, and good food. Sometimes people have to be in very strange places before they *really* understand that Christmas does not *depend* on any of these things.

Here is a story about a strange kind of Christmas. Read it and see whether or not you think the people in it really celebrated with true Christmas joy.

68

DR. MUELLER stood looking out of the door of a small wooden building. As far as he could see, other wooden buildings much like the one in which he stood stretched in rows off toward a high fence. Here and there in the fence were towers where guards kept watch day and night.

Off in the distance, too far for Dr. Mueller to see, there was a big gate. One day, months before, he had been brought in through that gate in a truck loaded with other men, women, and children. Prisoners of war they were, now locked in behind the great gate that shut them away from their families and their friends.

"How long have I been here?" wondered Dr. Mueller, as he turned to look at the rows of little scratches on the wooden wall beside the door. He began to count slowly—and then suddenly he stopped. He picked up the sharp stick with which he had made a mark on his "calendar" every day since he had been in the prison camp. He made a few quick marks over at the side and then he said, "Why, it's nearly Christmas! We must do something about that right away!"

Dr. Mueller tried to call to some of the other men, but began to cough so hard that he had to sit down on one of the hard beds to get his breath. When the coughing finally stopped, he sat still, remembering Christmas in the days before he had been brought to this terrible place and thinking of ways to celebrate it under the circumstances.

"I know what we'll do first," he thought. "We'll get together and tell each other what we remember best about Christmas." Soon Dr. Mueller had gathered about him a small group of men and women who were eager to remember other Christmases.

Two men kept watch so that the guards would not come upon them by surprise. Too many people talking together made the guards angry. "The prisoners are always thinking up crazy ways to get out of here," they said. "It saves a lot of trouble if we keep them from talking to each other."

Dr. Mueller told first of the church where he had been the minister. "Our service by candlelight on Christmas Eve was always the loveliest service of the whole year," he said.

"What I remember best is the nativity play given by the boys and girls in our church school each year," said one of the women.

A young man spoke next. "Going caroling was one of the nicest parts of Christmas for me," he said.

Just then the men who were keeping watch signaled that a guard was coming. The little group separated, but each one kept thinking about Christmas and what it had meant to him in the past.

They tried to share their memories with other prisoners, too. Some of them only replied, "It's no use remembering about Christmas. We should spend our time worrying about the enemy

planes that are coming in greater numbers every day. But what's the difference to us? We might as well be blown up as left to die in this prison."

But Dr. Mueller could not stop thinking about Christmas. Every day when he scratched another mark on the calendar beside the door, he knew that Christmas was one day closer. The week before Christmas he asked for permission to speak to the men in charge of the prison.

"Soon it will be Christmas," he said when he was brought before them. "Won't you do some little thing to make our buildings look more cheerful? It doesn't matter what you do, it's only that we should do something because it's Christmas."

"Bah! Christmas!" said the commander of the prison. "The best thing for you is to forget all about it. We don't celebrate Christmas here. Get back to your bed, old man, and be glad you've got one. Things could be worse for you. I thought you had something important to say. I don't want to hear any more talk about Christmas."

Sadly Dr. Mueller walked back toward his building. If he could only think of something. . . . Just then he saw a clump of tiny fir trees growing outside the corner of the fence. They looked like Christmas trees! This gave him an idea.

72

That evening young Hans would bring their supper. He was not as cross as the other guards. Maybe Hans would help!

Dr. Mueller could hardly wait till supper time. When Hans appeared, the minister spoke about the fir trees. "Could we have just one tree? The very smallest would do."

But Hans just laughed. "No tree, Dr. Mueller. There's no Christmas in a prison camp. Don't bother me about such a foolish thing."

"Just one or two branches then," begged Dr. Mueller. "If we could only have some very small thing to remind us of Christmas."

But Hans refused to be bothered. "There's no Christmas here," he said again, "not in this prison."

Dr. Mueller watched the guard walk away. "No Christmas here," he thought. "I guess he's right."

But as he sat thinking sadly how all his ideas had come to nothing, he suddenly wondered, "What is Christmas after all?" He began to hear in his mind the words, "To you is born this day . . . Christ the Lord. . . . Glory to God in the highest." More words came, words from the Bible, from Christmas carols, from the prayers he had prayed in his church at Christmas. And the more words he said, the more came to him. He became so excited he could hardly talk.

He waited for a chance to gather a little group of prisoners around him. "Let's try to remember all of the Christmas story," Dr. Mueller said. "I know some parts of it and you will know other parts. We will spend all the days between now and Christmas remembering the story of Jesus and why he came to earth. Let's do the same with some of the carols. Then on Christmas Day we will have a real celebration."

Many of the prisoners agreed. It became almost like a game for them because they had to work at it a little at a time, when the guards were not around. "Joy to the world! The Lord is come: Let earth receive her King," one person might remember, and then forget what came next. But soon another would be found who could go on with "Let every heart prepare him room, And heaven and nature sing."

Bit by bit, as they worked at it, they remembered all of the Christmas story as it is told in Matthew and Luke. Sharing what each could remember, all of them soon could sing five or six of the carols. And something began to happen to the people as they thought about Jesus and how his coming had made so much difference in the world. They no longer gave in to their sadness and hunger and sickness. There was a strange kind of joy in their days that they had not known since coming to the prison.

75

No one tried to explain it. They just felt it within themselves.

Christmas Day was cold and gloomy. The building was dark and cheerless, but the people were filled with a strange excitement. Whenever they could, they gathered in small groups, always with someone posted to watch for the guards. They repeated together the Bible stories. They sang the carols very softly. They prayed together.

Instead of one big service, they had many tiny, brief ones. It was as if they all shared one happy secret which gave them new courage and strength. Because everyone had helped to remember the Scripture and the carols, the service belonged to each person in a very special way.

That night, as Dr. Mueller lay on his hard bed in the cold building, he thought about the day. In spite of all the things they had missed, he was sure of one thing. "Christmas is first of all knowing about God's gift to us of Jesus, whose love makes all the difference in the world," he thought. "That's what made this Christmas one that none of us here will ever forget as long as we live. Somehow, in a strange sort of way, it's the *best* Christmas I have ever known."

76

A PRAYER FOR CHRISTMAS DAY

THANK YOU, God, for Christmas Day
　　When Jesus Christ was born.
THANK YOU for the angel's song
　　On that first Christmas morn.

THANK YOU for your love and care
　　That Jesus came to tell.
HELP OUR church to show your love
　　To people everywhere.

Written by a fourth-grade class

LET THE CHILDREN COME

Mrs. Patch looked out the window of her neat little trailer and frowned. "It's those Miller children again," she said to Mr. Patch who sat reading in his easy chair. "They don't have enough clothes on for this kind of weather. What's their mother thinking of?"

Mr. Patch looked up from his book. "Now, now, Hildy, stop fussing. You raised your own family and you can't go on mothering every child you see. Maybe Mrs. Miller thinks her children are dressed just right."

Mrs. Patch sniffed. "Dressed right," she said under her breath, "not even a jacket and it's almost freezing out." She went about her work, dusting and putting things in their place. But every now and then she would look out and see the Miller children playing in the cold.

Suddenly she pulled out the fold-up table, got out the flour sifter, reached for the sugar and flour, and said, "I guess I'll bake

some cookies. Maybe that Miller girl would like to come in and help me." Then Mrs. Patch started for the door.

Mr. Patch smiled a secret little smile and nodded his head. "Just had to think of some way to bring those kids in out of the cold," he said to himself. "Maybe I have a game the boy could play with me."

Soon the little trailer was full of the smell of fresh cookies, the sound of children's voices, and music, for the Miller children

loved to sing! In no time at all, it seemed, it began to get dark. Mrs. Patch had to say, "It's time to go home now, children. Take some cookies along with you." She watched them run off down the pathway, around the corner, and off toward the place where the Miller trailer was parked.

Mrs. Patch had not asked, "Why aren't you in school?" She had not said, "Come again tomorrow." The Patches had lived long enough in the trailer camp to know that most of their neighbors never really knew whether they would still be there tomorrow or whether they would be off looking for another crop to harvest or a field of fruit or vegetables to pick. Sometimes the children went to school, if the crop was a big one or if the farm had several crops to harvest at different times. But usually it wasn't worth starting because they would be moving to another farm so soon.

"We never intended to stay here," the Patches told their friends. "We parked here because the country is so beautiful. After a few weeks we didn't want to leave."

Soon after the Patches decided to stay for a while, they hunted up a church. On the first Sunday they felt a little strange. They had never moved before, and belonging to one church for nearly twenty-five years hadn't given them much practice at being strangers! The Patches were much better at greeting newcomers than at being new themselves. But the people were friendly, and after a few weeks they began to feel right at home.

Life for the Patches would have been just about perfect, except for one thing. The children! Not their own children—they were all grown up and married. It was the children of the migrant workers living at the edge of the trailer park that worried the Patches.

Day after day the story was the same—children without warm enough clothes, children who were big enough to be in school running around with nothing to do but get into trouble, children who never went to church school on Sunday, children whose parents cared but didn't know what to do to make matters better, and children whose parents didn't care at all.

"Somebody ought to do something," said Mrs. Patch. " I just can't stand seeing these children treated like that."

"Now, now, Hildy," Mr. Patch would say, "don't go stirring up something. Remember we're new here ourselves. People in this town have lived here a long time and they know what's going on. Maybe they *have* tried to do something."

"Well, then, they ought to try again," muttered Mrs. Patch as she dusted the back of the same chair for the third time.

It happened that the Miller family stayed on and on, and the Miller children became daily callers in the Patches' trailer. One Saturday afternoon, Mrs. Patch said, "Children, ask your mother whether you can go to church school with us tomorrow. It's the church on the corner of Vine Street across from the bank. We'll take you and bring you home again."

"Now, Hildy," said Mr. Patch when he heard what she had done, "you be careful. Don't you go stirring up something. How do you know those children are wanted in church school?"

"Wanted?" said Mrs. Patch. "Who ever heard of a church *not* wanting children? Why, there's even a big window in the church with 'Let the children come' in big blue letters on it! Of course they want children in our church."

But on Monday morning Mrs. Patch was not so sure. The Miller children had gone to church school, but they said they didn't want to go again.

When Mrs. Patch called the church to find out what had happened, the minister said he would come to see her. That morning Mrs. Patch learned that some of the people felt the church school was already so crowded that if the children of the migrant workers came, there just would not be enough room.

"I wish we could do something for the families out here," said the minister looking out of the trailer window. "I've tried, Mrs. Patch, but I can't do it alone. And no one else seems to have the time or the interest."

On Monday afternoon the minister found out that the Patches had lots of time, and that they certainly were interested! So for the

rest of that week there was a great deal of scrubbing and cleaning and painting going on in a little room in the church basement that had not been used for years.

And all that week there was a great deal of visiting in the trailer homes by the Patches. On the following Sunday morning a car filled with children, some scrubbed and dressed by their parents and some scrubbed by the Patches, arrived at the church. They went to the little room that smelled of fresh paint and looked as gay and cheerful as could be!

86

As the weeks went by, everyone in the church learned about the little room that somehow had been nicknamed "Patches' Parlor." Mrs. Patch told a women's meeting about it and they even surprised themselves by voting to give twenty-five dollars to buy new chairs. Mr. Patch sat beside a lumber yard owner at a men's meeting and came away with the promise of all the scrap wood he could use for a workshop during the week. Two of the church school teachers called Mrs. Patch to ask why the smallest children didn't come to the church nursery where there were toys they could play with. And the leader of the children's choir heard the Miller children singing and asked them to come to choir practice on Saturday.

One night when spring had come, Mr. Patch stood outside their little trailer looking up at the sky. Mrs. Patch came to the door. "Wishing on a star?" she asked.

Mr. Patch shook his head. "I can't think of anything to wish for," he said. "Can you?"

Mrs. Patch thought for a moment. "Just one thing. I wish we could get rid of Patches' Parlor."

"Get rid of it," said Mr. Patch in surprise. "Why, Hildy, I thought you wanted a place for our children to go to church school. Why do you want to get rid of our little room?"

"Because our children shouldn't be off by themselves, that's why," said Mrs. Patch. "They need to be mixed in with everyone else. Then maybe some of their parents would come to church. Our children need to know that they are part of the whole church just like everyone else. After all, in that story Jesus didn't say,

'Let the children come to me, but keep some of them over to one side!' "

Mr. Patch didn't say anything, but the next day he called the minister. "I've decided that I will accept your invitation to have my name put on the list of officers for the people to vote on," he said.

Not very long afterwards, Mr. Patch was chosen an officer in the church. And not very long after that, when there was a special day for children in the church, Mrs. Patch got her wish. The church school superintendent said there was to be a new way of dividing into classes so that some rooms would not be so full and others nearly empty. And when the list of rooms and classes was read out, Patches' Parlor wasn't even mentioned!

Later that morning Mrs. Patch was standing beside Mr. Patch as they sang a hymn in the church service. "Tell me the stories of Jesus," they sang, and the sun coming through the stained glass windows made the words "Let the children come" shine out of one window in a special way. Mrs. Patch stopped singing and just looked at the words.

When the hymn was finished, she leaned over to Mr. Patch and said, "I've just had an idea. Why don't we get some books for Patches' Parlor and make it into a sort of reading room where our children can go after school or on Saturdays to practice their reading and writing? Then they won't feel so far behind the other boys and girls when they *do* go to school. Maybe more would go then. I could help a couple of days a week!"

Mr. Patch smiled and said, "Now, now, Hildy. Don't you go stirring things up around here. But I'll see what I can do!"

A POEM

THE LORD is ever near,
He bids his children pray;
While they are speaking he will hear,
And bless them day by day.

OUR FATHER'S love is sure,
And very wise his care;
He gives us what he knows is best,
And hears our every prayer.

WORD LIST

NAMES OF PEOPLE

A′ bra-ham
Jer′ e-mi′ ah
Bar′ uch (bar′ uk)
Je-hoi′ a-kim
Zed′ e-ki′ ah
Saul
Paul
Ste′ phen (Stē′ ven)
Te-lem′ a-chus

NAMES OF PLACES

Hā′ ran
Je-ru′ sa-lem (je-roo′ sa-lem)
Rōme

OTHER NEW WORDS

na′ tion (na′ shun)
tribes′ man
graz′ ing
bless′ ed
proph′ et (prof′ et)
dic′ tate